MW00885192

hello beautiful badass!

Manifest good vibes and self love with some positive profanity! Relax and color each page while you breathe in the good shit and exhale the bullshit. The affirmations inside this book will encourage you to embrace your badassery so you can tell any negative thoughts to fuck off!

Follow Sweary Indigo on Facebook for even more positive profanity!

Copyright © 2020 by Sweary Indigo.
All rights reserved. No part of this book may be reproduced in any manner without written permission.

I attract
good shit
into my life

I tell negative
thoughts to
fuck off

I'm a direct
descendant
of badassery

I throw kindness
around like
fucking confetti

I'm in alignment
as fuck with my
soul's purpose

I give myself
permission to do
whatever the fuck
is right for me

swearing keeps
my throat
chakra clear

happiness is
my fucking
birthright

I invite gratitude into my badass heart

I have the
power to create
kick ass changes

I don't have
to apologize
for being a
badass bitch

I live my life
as if anything is
fucking possible

I'm doing a beautiful job at figuring out some heavy shit

I'm allowed
to say no
to bullshit

If I can
dream it, I can
fucking do it

I am confident
enough to do the
shit that's good
for my soul

I accept and
love my badass
self, just the
way I am

I forgive myself
for any and all
past fuck ups

when it rains,
I look for
fucking rainbows

I was given this
life because I'm
strong enough
to fucking live it

I am always
safe and
protected
from bullshit

I'm surrounded
by love and
awesome shit

I let go of
worries and
replace them
with flying fucks

I will not give up,
I have a lot of
motherfuckers
to prove wrong

I'm allowed to
set boundaries
with bitches that
stress me out

just because my
path is different
doesn't mean
I'm fucking lost

I am awesome
and I will keep
that shit up

I let go of
clusterfucks
that no longer
serve me

I am a
magnet for
motherfucking
miracles

I become more badass with each passing day

it's never too
late to get my
shit together

I will not
compare
myself to
dumbasses

my heart is
overflowing with
fucking joy

zen as fuck
is my primary
state of being

I take action
and get shit
done to achieve
my goals

I put my
heart and soul
into all the
shit that I do

I'm a problem
solver, that's
how I've made it
this fucking far

I am kind and
loving, but I
take no shit

I search
for the good
in every
shit show

my creativity
is fucking
magical

Made in United States
Cleveland, OH
14 December 2024